Young Readers' Series

ADIÓS CHI CHI

The Adventures of a Tarantula

Carol A. Amato
Illustrated by David Wenzel

FOREST HOUSE ®

School & Library Edition

This book is dedicated to
Chantell and Dominique
who make teaching a joy.

Text © Copyright 1996 by Carol A. Amato
Illustrations © Copyright 1996 by David Wenzel

All inquiries should be addressed to:
Barron's Educational Series, Inc.
250 Wireless Boulevard
Hauppauge, New York 11788

International Standard Book No. 0-8120-9506-5

Library of Congress Catalog Card No. 95-38796
Library of Congress Cataloging-in-Publication Data

Amato, Carol A.
    Adios Chi Chi : the adventures of a tarantula / Carol A. Amato ; illustrated by
David Wenzel.
        p. cm.—(Young readers' series)
    Summary: When she unexpectedly finds a tarantula, Maria keeps it temporarily
as a pet, learning about its physical characteristics, habits, and needs in captivity.
    ISBN 0-8120-9506-5
    1. Tarantulas—Juvenile literature. 2. Tarantulas as pets—Juvenile literature.
[1. Tarantulas. 2. Spiders. 3. Tarantulas as pets.] I. Wenzel, David, 1950–, ill. II. Title.
III. Series: Amato, Carol A.—Young readers' series.
QL458.42.T5A47 1996
595.4'4—dc20
                                                                95-38796
                                                                    CIP
                                                                    AC

PRINTED IN HONG KONG
6789 9955 987654321

Table of Contents

1

Moving Day

After dinner, María went to her room to finish packing. Before long, she was done. She went to her window. The setting summer sun made the sky over her New Mexico home watermelon red. Everything was so pretty. Her eyes filled with tears.

"No matter what Mamá says, no place will be like New Mexico," she thought.

The next day, María and her family traveled by airplane to their new home in New York City. A moving truck would bring the rest of their things in a few days. They arrived at their apartment building late at night. María and her brother José carefully explored each room.

"María," said her father. "There's a wonderful garden in the backyard. We were lucky to get this apartment on the first floor."

"That's nice," she said.

María was still too sad to be interested in their new home. The family was so tired from the long trip that they went to bed without unpacking.

The next day, María woke up early. She ate breakfast
as quickly as she could. She was feeling a little better
about her new home and wanted to explore the backyard
garden.

"Before you go out, María, please unpack your
suitcase," said her mother.

"Oh, all right," María said.

She went to her bedroom and put her suitcase on
her bed.

"Let's see," she said to herself. "I'll put my jeans and
shorts in the bottom drawer. I think I'll put my. . ."

María jumped back from her suitcase. On top of her
favorite blue shirt was a huge spider!

"What's *that* doing here?" she asked out loud.

"Mamá, Mamá!" she shouted as she ran to the kitchen.

"There's a monster spider in my suitcase!"

"*Hija*, calm down," said her mother. "I'll come and see."

The spider had not moved. It was enormous. Its body was a few inches long, and it was brown and hairy all over.

"María, that is no monster spider," said her mother. "It's a tarantula. Did you forget the tarantulas that live in New Mexico?"

"But Mamá, what's a tarantula doing in New York City?"

"Well, María, it seems that *this* tarantula came with us in your suitcase," laughed her mother.

"Mamá, this isn't funny. It won't be able to find anything to eat here," María said.

"You're right, María, but I have an idea. We are
going back to New Mexico to visit *Abuelo and Abuela*
in three months. We can keep the spider for now and
bring it back when we go there."

"Oh, boy!" said María. "We just got here and I
already have a pet."

"You know, María, in a way, the tarantula will be
our first friend in our new home!" said her mother.

"Mamá, where will we keep the tarantula?" asked María.

"For now, let's put it in a box," said her mother. María and her mother found a small box and put a window screen on top of it. The tarantula still had not moved. María's mother slid a long piece of cardboard under the tarantula and slowly began to place it into the box.

"Be careful, Mamá. The spider might bite you," said María.

"I am being careful, *hija*," said her mother. "Fill a small dish with water. The tarantula must be thirsty after that long trip."

Later in the day, María and her mother brought the tarantula to a nearby pet store. María explained to the shop owner how they had found it and then told him they wanted to keep it as a pet.

"I can help you," the shop owner said. "I see you have a beautiful female, or girl, spider there. It's called a North American brown tarantula."

"How can you tell it's a girl?" asked María.

"Well," said the shop owner, "yours is about 3 inches (7 centimeters) long. That's about the right size for a full grown female's body. Because the male, or boy, is only about 2 inches (5.0 centimeters) long, this must be a female. Also, yours has pretty short legs, and the male's legs are long."

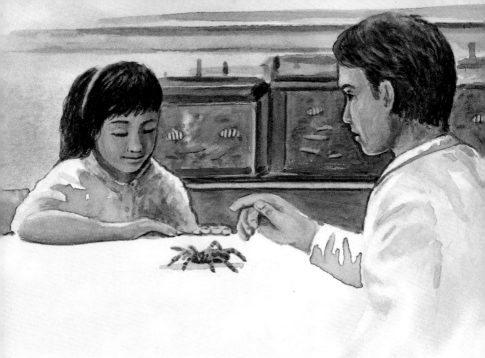

"What should we feed her?" asked María.

"Tarantulas eat only live food," the shop owner said.
"I will sell you crickets. If you can find other small
insects, she will also eat them. Feed her once a week.
You will see that your tarantula will use her fangs to
make a hole in the insect. Through her fangs, poison
goes into the insect and softens the insect's insides.
Then the tarantula sucks out the juice."

"That's some juice drink," laughed María's mother.

"You will need to set up a good home for your pet,"
said the salesman. He brought out a 5-gallon (19 liter)
tank and put gravel on the bottom of it.

"Can I pick her up?" asked María.

"She may become very tame if you handle her often
and gently. Like some people, some tarantulas are
unfriendly. A tarantula's fangs are half an inch (1.3
centimeters) long, and it *will* use them for protection!
The poison in the fangs can kill only the small creatures
it eats. To a person, the bite feels like a bee sting."

He showed María how to pick up the tarantula.

"Slowly put your hand, palm up, near the spider. Wait a little to see if she is calm. Then, gently slide your hand under her and lift her up."

María did as he said and lifted the spider into her new home. The shop owner covered the tank with a top containing airholes.

"Have fun with your new pet!" he said, as they left the store.

"*Gracias*," said María and her mother.

"And *gracias* to you !" said the shop owner.

As soon as María and her mother opened the door to their apartment, they called Papá and José to come meet the new visitor.

"María, let me see! Let me see! What is it? Where did you get it?"

María proudly explained how she had found the tarantula and what she had learned at the pet store. Then with José's help, she carried the tank into the garden. Together they found some small rocks and put them into the tank. Soon, she was back in the house calling her mother.

"Mamá, José's bothering me. Tell him to leave me alone."

"María, thank him for his help, and tell him to come into the kitchen."

Back in the garden, she talked to the tarantula.

"Perhaps you'd like to make a hiding place," she said.

"Now, what shall I name you?" María thought and thought. She thought so hard, in fact, that she fell fast asleep.

"María, come in for dinner," called her mother. María woke up. Suddenly, a name for the spider came to her.

"I know! I'll call you Chi Chi. That's the name of my best friend in New Mexico, and you are my best friend now."

María carried the tank inside. The family was sitting at the table.

"I'm going to name my tarantula, Chi Chi," she said. "Look! Chi Chi made a hiding place with the rocks I put in her tank."

"Mamá, Papá, do tarantulas spin webs? Where do they live? How do they breathe?"

Her mother and father shook their heads. "We don't know," said her father. "I guess it's time for a trip to the library so we can find out!"

In the library the next day, they found many children's books about spiders. María and her father sat at a table and began to read them.

"Wow!" said María. "There are so many different kinds of tarantulas! Look at these pictures, Papá. Some of the tarantulas shown are black. This one is kind of blue, and that one has red knees. This book says that the thirty kinds of tarantulas in the United States are the largest spiders in our country. There are many more in the warmest parts of the world. Some of them are so large that they eat animals such as lizards, frogs, and snakes!"

"Listen to this, María!" said her father. "It says here that tarantulas have lived since before the days of the dinosaurs. Did you know that they are not insects? Insects have six legs, but spiders have eight legs. Also, tarantulas and other burrowing spiders can't spin webs like other spiders and so must live underground."

"I never knew that spiders were not insects," said María. "Can we take these books home, Papá?"

"Of course. You can get a library card today and sign them out."

"Great," said María. "I want to learn more about Chi Chi."

María rushed through the door when they got home. Mamá was reading a book to José.

"*Hola* Mamá. *Hola* José," said María. "Look at all the books we found about tarantulas!"

"Did you find out where tarantulas live?" asked her mother.

"Yes, we did," said Maria. "We found out that the place where something lives is called its habitat. The brown tarantula's habitat is in the southwestern United States. That's where we used to live. Tarantulas like warm places. It makes its home in deserts, woods, and grassy places."

"What kind of house does a tarantula have?" asked José.

"Well, it's not exactly a house!" laughed María. She opened one of the books.

"Look at this picture," she said. "The tarantula digs a burrow or hole in the ground. The burrow can be as deep as 1 foot (30 centimeters). Then it goes sideways for 1 to 2 feet (30 to 60 centimeters). The tarantula lines the burrow with silk so the walls won't cave in. She also spins a silk cocoon for her eggs. The silk come out of a part of her body called the spinnerets.

"I also found out that tarantulas live in groups and may live close together on a hillside."

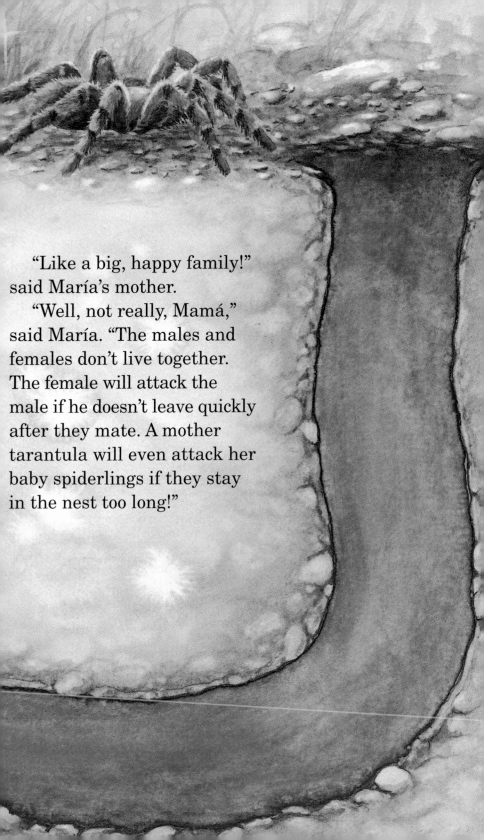

"Like a big, happy family!" said María's mother.

"Well, not really, Mamá," said María. "The males and females don't live together. The female will attack the male if he doesn't leave quickly after they mate. A mother tarantula will even attack her baby spiderlings if they stay in the nest too long!"

"Oh my," María's mother said. "It's a good thing we're not tarantulas, or I'd be attacking both of you right now! I guess people and spiders don't act in the same ways."

"That's true, Mamá. The tarantulas are not being mean. They are behaving like tarantulas."

"You know, I also read that we must protect tarantulas. There are not as many tarantulas as there once were. People have made roads and buildings on the tarantulas' habitats. Without places for them to live, they may someday die out and become extinct."

"Does it matter if tarantulas become extinct? Why do we need tarantulas?" asked José.

"Tarantulas and other spiders help to keep the balance in nature. By eating insects, they help to be sure there are not too many insects. We learned in school that every living thing has a part to play in nature," María replied.

After lunch, María brought Chi Chi and her books into the garden. José played nearby.

"*Hija!*" her mother called after her. "Come in and clean your messy room."

When María went back inside, José walked over to the tank.

"*Hola* Chi Chi," he said. "María will not mind if I play with you."

He put his hand into the tank. Chi Chi backed away. José tried to grab her. Suddenly, the spider jumped forward and bit his hand.

José yelled, "Mamá, Mamá! Chi Chi bit me!" He ran indoors.

"Calm down, *hijo*," his mother said. "Sit still while I clean the bite and put ice on it. It is not so bad."

María came running from her room.

"I told you never to touch Chi Chi!" she said angrily to José. "You were not careful, and she was only protecting herself."

José began to cry. The bite didn't hurt much, but María's words did.

SPINNERETS

ABDOMEN

"I didn't mean to yell at you, José. Are you OK?"

"I'm OK, María," he answered. "I promise not to bother Chi Chi again. Could you tell me more about tarantulas?"

María took José's hand. "Come with me," she said.

They sat down next to Chi Chi's tank. María opened one of the books.

"Look, José," said María. "Here's a picture of a tarantula that shows its body parts. The tarantula's body has two parts, the front and the rear. There are eight eyes in front, but they're not much good.

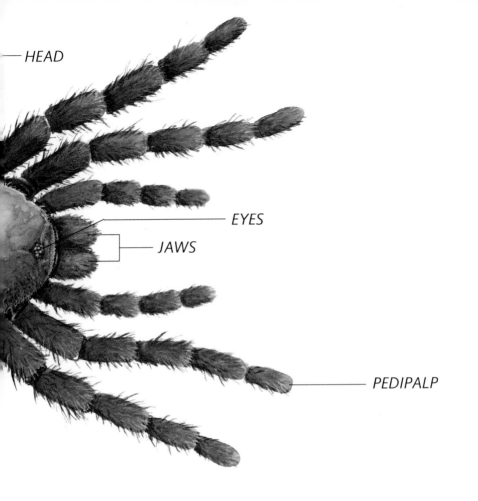

HEAD

EYES

JAWS

PEDIPALP

A tarantula can see only about 3 feet (90 centimeters) in front of itself!"

"Maybe it should wear four tiny pairs of eyeglasses!" laughed José. "Why is it so hairy?" he asked.

"The tarantula has thousands of hairs, called kicking hairs," answered María. "It can rub its back pair of legs against its body and fling its hairs at its enemy. The hairs sting and can cause a rash."

"I'm glad she didn't fling her hairs at me too!" laughed José.

"What are those?" José asked, pointing to the picture.

"Those are the pedipalps, or foot-feelers. They are used for holding food and for telling the spider what it is touching," said María.

"This part is cool, José. The book says that in order to grow, a tarantula has to shed, or get rid of, its hard shell. The shell is called an exoskeleton. Can you say this big word, José?"

"Ex-o-skel-e-ton!" said José.

"Great!" said María. "Listen to this! There is a new shell that takes the place of the old one. It has *all* new body parts! Chi Chi will grow like this many times in her life. She could live to be more than twenty years old, but the males live only ten or twelve years."

"I guess it's better to be a female tarantula!" laughed José.

The rest of the summer went by very quickly for María. She saw children playing in her neighborhood, but she was too shy to meet them.

Soon the first day of school arrived. In her classroom, the children laughed and joked with one another. They didn't seem to even know she was there. When she came home from school, she told her mother about her unhappy day.

"I know how you must feel, María. It isn't always easy to make new friends," said her mother. "I do have a good idea, though. I can call your teacher and ask her if you can bring Chi Chi to school tomorrow to meet the other children."

"That would be great, Mamá!"

Her mother called María's teacher. Ms. Gibbons thought it would be a wonderful idea if María taught the children all about Chi Chi.

The next morning, with José's help, María carried
the tank into the classroom. The other children all
gathered around her.

34

"Sit down, children," said Ms. Gibbons. "María has something special to show you."

María smiled shyly and uncovered the tank. One of the girls screamed. A boy shouted, "That's a killer spider!"

"Don't worry," said María. "It won't hurt you. This is my pet tarantula, Chi Chi."

The children had many questions about tarantulas. María remembered everything she and her father had read. Everyone in the class was amazed at how much she knew about tarantulas. Answering the questions, María forgot all about being shy. She also told the class that she would soon be returning Chi Chi to her real habitat.

"Will Chi Chi have baby spiders when she goes back to New Mexico?" asked Brad.

"She probably will some day," answered María. "Female tarantulas don't have babies until they're ten or twelve. They lay from a hundred to a thousand eggs! When the spiderlings hatch, they leave home as fast as they can!"

"Doesn't the mother take care of them?" asked Kate.

"Not exactly," said María. "If the spiderlings stick around too long, she will eat them! But don't worry. They can take care of themselves right away. Even so, many get eaten by insects. That's why she lays so many eggs."

"Remember, children," said Ms. Gibbons, "wild creatures were not meant to behave as we do!"

When María finished talking to the class, all her classmates clapped their hands.

María made many new friends that day!

The months passed. It was nearly time for María and her family to visit her *abuelos* in New Mexico. María had missed them and wanted to see them, but she was also sad. Soon she would be releasing Chi Chi into her habitat. María's parents saw how sad she was.

"If you want, you can keep Chi Chi," her father told her. "Because tarantulas live so long, some people keep them as pets for many years."

"No, Papá. Chi Chi must be free to find a mate and to have spiderlings. She must live the life of a tarantula."

"I am proud that you care enough about Chi Chi to let her go," said her mother.

The day for the trip arrived. Chi Chi, already an experienced traveler, would ride with María in the passenger section of the airplane. When the airplane landed, the tarantula was just fine.

When they arrived at her grandparents' house, María asked, "*Abuelos,* would you mind if Chi Chi lived in your backyard?"

"That will be just fine, María," said her *abuela*. "But Chi Chi may leave our backyard and live someplace else."

"I know," said María. "But she just might make her home here. Then I could come back to see her."

María took the tank into a far corner of the backyard. She gently lifted Chi Chi out of the tank. María had tears in her eyes.

"It's time for me to go, Chi Chi. I will miss you. You were my first friend in my new home. Now you will be free to live a tarantula's life."

María placed her hand on the grass. Chi Chi slowly climbed across her fingers. She carefully felt the grass with her foot-feelers. Then she quickly ran behind some rocks several feet away. María called after her, "*Adiós* Chi Chi! Good-bye! If you live here, I will be back to visit you. And please, try not to eat any of your babies!" she said, laughing.

Cautiously, Chi Chi walked to a nearby mound of sand and began digging.

Afterword

Spiders live almost everywhere on Earth—from jungles and swamps, seashores and deserts to mountain tops. Wherever you live, you will probably find spiders in your house or in your backyard. There are so many spiders, it is hard to keep track of them all. In the tarantula family alone, there are 800 different kinds! Spiders come in many shapes and sizes. Some are as tiny as a speck of dust. Some are as big as a frisbie. Scientists are still discovering new kinds of spiders.

Many people don't like spiders. They may be afraid of them, and think they look ugly and scary. While a few spiders can be dangerous (like the black widow), most spiders are harmless. What most people don't know is that if spiders disappeared from the Earth, we would soon miss them. They play a very important role in our lives. Spiders eat insects that are harmful to crops and people. Spiders are also food for animals such as birds. Removing spiders from the world would upset the balance in nature.

Watch a spider sometime. You will see that it is very interesting. Look for their amazing webs outside when the weather is warm. Learn more about our eight-legged friends!

Glossary

abuela (ah-boo-A-la) Spanish term for grandmother.

abuelo (ah-boo-A-lo) Spanish term for grandfather.

adiós (ah-thee-OHS) Spanish term for good-bye.

balance (BAL-ance) keeping something equal so that there is neither too little nor too much. When one animal eats another animal, it helps to keep the balance in nature. Without this balance, there would be too many of one kind of animal and not enough of another.

black widow spider (WID-oh) the female black widow spider is black with red markings. She is very poisonous, and eats the male spider after mating!

exoskeleton (ex-o-SKEL-e-ton) the hard skin or shell on many boneless animals such as insects, spiders, and crustaceans (crabs and lobsters). These creatures shed their exoskeleton in order to grow. This way of growing is called *molting* (MOLT-ing).

extinct (ex-TINCT) when a living thing is no longer living anywhere on Earth.

foot-feelers (foot-FEEL-ers), or pedipalps, a pair of leg-like feelers on a spider's front section that are used to hold food and to identify objects.

gracias (GRAH-ci-ahs) Spanish term for thank you.

hija (EE-ha) Spanish term for daughter.

hijo (EE-ho) Spanish term for son.

hola (OH-la) Spanish term for hello.

mate animals must find a partner, or mate, in order to have babies.

New Mexico (New MEX-i-co) a state in the southwestern United States.

North America (North A-MER-i-ca) the northern continent in the western part of the world.

Southwestern United States (south-WEST-ern u-NI-ted States) the states in which tarantulas are most numerous: Arizona, Nevada, New Mexico, southern California, Utah, and Colorado. Tarantulas can also be found in Kansas, Oklahoma, Mississippi, Arkansas, Louisiana, Tennessee, and Florida.

spinnerets (spinn-er-ETS) glands on a spider's abdomen that, through many tiny tubes, release the liquid silk used to spin the spider's thread.

tropical (TROP-i-cal) hot and humid places nearest to the equator (the imaginary circle around the Earth that divides it into northern and southern parts, or hemispheres).

Dear Parents and Educators:

Welcome to the Young Readers' series!

These learning stories have been created to introduce young children to the study of animals.

Children's earliest exposure to reading is usually through fiction. Stories read aloud invite children into the world of words and imagination. If children are read to frequently, this becomes a highly anticipated form of entertainment. Often that same pleasure is felt when children learn to read on their own. Nonfiction books are also read aloud to children but generally when they are older. However, interest in the "real" world emerges early in life, as soon as children develop a sense of wonder about everything around them.

There are a number of excellent read-aloud natural-science books available. Educators and parents agree that children love nonfiction books about animals. Unfortunately, there are very few that can be read *by* young children. One of the goals of the Young Readers' series is to happily fill that gap!

Adiós Chi Chi is one in a series of learning stories designed to appeal to young readers. In the classroom, the series can be incorporated into literature-based or whole-language programs, and would be especially suitable for science theme teaching units. Within planned units, each book may serve as a springboard to immersion techniques that include hands-on activities, field study trips, and additional research and reading. Many of the books are also concerned with the threatened or endangered status of the species studied and the role even young people can play in the preservation plan.

These books can also serve as read-aloud for young children. Weaving information through a story form lends itself easily to reading aloud. Hopefully, this book and others in the series will provide entertainment and wonder for both young readers and listeners.

C.A.

Guidelines for the Young Readers' Series

In the Classroom

One of the goals of this series is to introduce the young child to factual information related to the species being studied. The science terminology used is relevant to the learning process for the young student. In the classroom, you may want to use multi-modality methods to ensure understanding and word recognition. The following suggestions may be helpful:

1. Refer to the pictures when possible for difficult words and discuss how these words can be used in another context.

2. Encourage the children to use word and sentence contextual clues when approaching unknown words. They should be encouraged to use the glossary since it is an important information adjunct to the story.

3. After the children read the story or individual chapter, you may want to involve them in discussions using a variety of questioning techniques:
    a. Questions requiring *recall* ask the children about past experiences, observations, or feelings. (*Have you ever seen movies or TV programs about tarantulas?*)
    b. *Process* questions help the children to discover relationships by asking them to compare, classify, infer, or explain. (*Do you have to eat every day? Does the tarantula? Why or why not?*)
    c. *Application* questions ask children to use new information in a hypothetical situation by evaluating, imagining, or predicting.

At Home

The above aids can be used if your child is reading independently or aloud. Children will also enjoy hearing this story read aloud to them. You may want to use some of the questioning suggestions above. The story may provoke many questions from your child. Stop and answer the questions. Replying with an honest, "I don't know," provides a wonderful opportunity to head for the library to do some research together!

Have a wonderful time in your shared quest of discovery learning!

Carol A. Amato
Language-Learning Specialist